if your child stutters

a guide for parents

revised edition

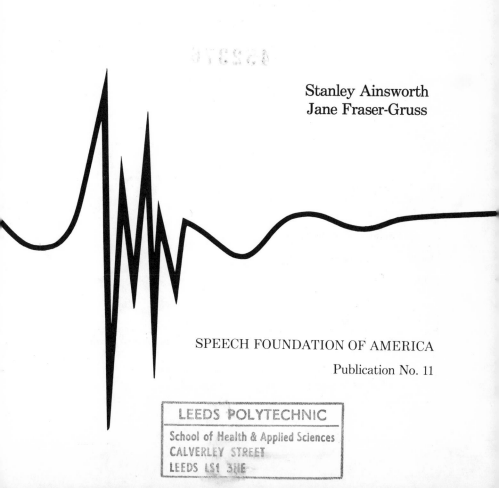

Stanley Ainsworth
Jane Fraser-Gruss

SPEECH FOUNDATION OF AMERICA

Publication No. 11

First Printing—1977
Second Printing—1978
Third Printing—1981

Speech Foundation of America
P.O. Box 11749
Memphis, Tennessee 38111

ISBN 0-933388-16-0

To the Parent

This book is written for parents who are concerned about the speech of their young child. If you have a child who usually speaks well but sometimes repeats words, sounds, or syllables, you may be afraid he is beginning to stutter.

The goal of this book is to enable you to begin working with your child, and the clinician when necessary, with a better understanding of the problem. It represents the thoughts of many experts in the field of stuttering, all of whom attach great importance to early intervention and prevention of stuttering in the young child.

Speech handicaps can be among the most frustrating and demoralizing known to man, particularly when neglected or misunderstood. For this reason, every effort towards a deeper understanding of them will contribute significantly to your child's normal, healthy development and well-being.

Jane Fraser-Gruss
Associate Director

Speech Foundation of America

Conference Panel

Stanley Ainsworth, Ph.D., Author and Chairman
> Alumni Foundation Distinguished Professor Emeritus of Speech Correction; formerly Associate Dean for Research and Graduate Studies, University of Georgia. Past President and Executive Vice-President, American Speech-Language-Hearing Association.

Carl Dell, Jr. M.A.
> Formerly Specialist in Stuttering Therapy, Grand Rapids, Michigan Schools.

Jane Fraser-Gruss, Co-author
> Associate Director, Speech Foundation of America.

Malcolm Fraser
> Director, Speech Foundation of America.

Harold L. Luper, Ph.D.
> Professor and Head, Department of Audiology and Speech Pathology, University of Tennessee. Fellow, and formerly Vice-President for Administration, American Speech-Language-Hearing Association. Co-author, *Stuttering: Therapy for Children.*

David Prins, Ph.D.
> Professor and Chairman, Department of Speech and Hearing Sciences, University of Washington, Seattle.

Conference Panel

Harold B. Starbuck, Ph.D.

>Formerly Professor and Chairman, Department of Speech Pathology and Audiology and Director, Speech and Hearing Clinic; formerly Director Summer Residence Stuttering Clinic, State University of New York, Geneseo, New York.

C. Woodruff Starkweather, Ph.D.

>Chairman, Speech Sciences Division, Temple University, Philadelphia, Pennsylvania. Editor, *Stuttering: An Account of Intensive Demonstration Therapy.*

Charles Van Riper, Ph.D.

>Distinguished Professor Emeritus and formerly Head, Department of Speech Pathology and Audiology, Western Michigan University. Honors of the American Speech and Hearing Association and formerly Councilor and Associate Editor. Author, *the Treatment of Stuttering.*

Dean Williams, Ph.D.

>Professor Speech Pathology and Audiology, University of Iowa. Fellow and formerly Councilor, American Speech-Language-Hearing Association. Editorial Board, *Journal of Communication Disorders.*

The speech of the children of man is our interest; and the communion of man is our concern. We seek out those who are halting in speech; and we offer help to those whose ears have been confused by disease. Life without speech is empty; and life devoid of communication is scarcely better than death. Therefore the duty we owe is sacred; and our calling is gravely important.

Robert W. West

Does My Child Stutter?

Speech begins with the first cry at birth. It then develops rapidly during the first two years as the child learns to make meaningful sounds and words. Later, between the ages of two and six, he may begin to have noticeable difficulties in speaking smoothly and freely, especially when starting to use sentences. All children repeat words and phrases, hesitate often and have occasional difficulty with the smooth flow of words, but some have more trouble than others, and for longer periods of time. If your child is one of these, you may wonder if he is beginning to stutter. Will it get worse or will it go away? If you think your child is stuttering, should you do something, and if so, what? Our aim is to answer some of these questions.

Is He Stuttering?

Stuttering interrupts the flow of speech, but so do many things. All of us repeat words or syllables occasionally; no one has speech that is perfectly smooth. We all hesitate, insert noises or words, get syllables mixed up, go back and revise sentences, or try to say two words at the same time and end up confused or stuck for an instant. The young child who is still struggling to master certain sounds, vocabulary, sentence arrangement and the social pressures of talking will naturally stumble more often than do adults and older children. The smoothness of everyone's speech also varies tremendously with external circumstances and internal feelings. These fluctuations in fluency are far greater in the young child.

Because children with normal disfluencies show many of the same behaviors found in stuttering, it may be difficult for you to distinguish normal stumblings from stuttering. Moreover, these vary in severity and frequency depending on time, circumstance, and the feelings of the speaker. Therefore, if you are concerned about your child's speech, it is probably best to let the speech-language pathologist* make the decision. If he concludes that your child is not abnormally disfluent, he will suggest that you take no action, although you may need to reduce your own anxiety. If your child is developing real difficulties however, the suggestions in this book as well as those of the clinician should be helpful to you.

How Does the Clinician Decide if Your Child Is Beginning to Stutter?

There are signs which show that your child has moved beyond the type of speech interruptions that are normal for his age. During the conference with the clinician, your child may not display some or even any of the things that have concerned you. If you are familiar with the signs of early stuttering however, you will be able to tell him when and if your child has been using them. Your day-to-day contact with your child makes you the best judge of how often and consistently they occur. An understanding of these signs will also help you decide whether or not a visit to the clinician is necessary.

---

*The speech-language pathologist will be referred to throughout this book as the clinician for editorial reasons.

Warning Signs[*]

Stuttering is more than just disruptions in the smooth flow of words, which we refer to as disfluencies. It is also made up of emotional reactions to the trouble experienced in speaking. When you consider these signs, try to avoid becoming too conscious of them. They need to be seen in relation to the total speech, most of which is probably quite fluent. Also keep in mind that many of these behaviors come and go. They occur at times in children who are never thought of as stutterers.

1. Multiple Repetitions

All of us, particularly children learning to talk, repeat words and phrases. It is not uncommon for a four-year old to repeat one word many times. One child, who was not a stutterer, repeated "and-and-and-and-and . . ." so many times that he forgot what he wanted to say. Fortunately he laughed about it and so did his parents.

Sometimes "starter" words or sounds such as a prolonged or repeated "uh" or "um" are used. More importantly, parts of words, usually the first syllable, may be repeated. If your child begins to use these repetitions often with many words and in many situations, he may be having more than the usual difficulty with his speech. The use of these syllabic repetitions may be a passing phase very much like periods of awkwardness in learning to walk and run. It is, however, one of the first signs the clinician looks for to see if your child may be stuttering.

---

[*]These warning, or danger signs, with some modification of headings, are also presented in a film entitled "The Prevention of Stuttering: Part I. Identifying the Danger Signs," produced by the Speech Foundation of America. If you can arrange to view it, you will see dramatic illustrations that will assist you in making decisions. It can be rented or purchased from Seven Oaks Productions, 9145 Sligo Creek Parkway, Silver Spring, Maryland 20910. Perhaps your local school system or Speech and Hearing Clinic, or a nearby college or university, can arrange for a showing of it to interested parents.

2. Schwa Vowel

The schwa (or weak) vowel is used throughout everyday speech. It is a neutral "uh" sound normally found in unaccented syllables such as "around," "concerned," "suggest," "wanted," "the boy." The child who is beginning to show more than the normal repetitions often uses the schwa in a way that delays and distorts the flow of speech. If he says "go-go-go-goat," we don't worry. But if he says "guh-guh-goat," we identify this as a warning sign, particularly if he cuts off the sound between syllables and thus "breaks" them by a series of "uh" (schwa) sounds. In words that begin with a vowel, such as "over," he may say, "uh-uh-uh-over" instead of repeating the initial sound "o". You may have difficulty in distinguishing these differences, but the clinician is trained to do so.

3. Prolongations

Sometimes, instead of repeating initial sounds, your child may prolong the first sound of a word, so that "Mommy" becomes "Mmmmmmmmmommy".

These first three signs—repeating sounds, repeating the schwa, prolonging sounds—may occur occasionally in nearly all children. If they begin to occur too frequently in too many speaking situations, and begin to affect your child's ability to communicate, you should be concerned.

4. Tremors

Occasionally you may notice that the small muscles around your child's mouth and jaw tremble or vibrate when he seems to get stuck on words. The degree of tremor may be mild or intense. These tremors are associated with difficulties in moving forward with speech when his mouth is held in one position with no sound coming out. The clinician will want to know how often you have noticed these tremors and if they appear to be lasting longer now than before.

5. Rise in Pitch and Loudness

As your child tries to get a word out, the pitch and loudness of the sound that he is prolonging may rise before he finishes the word. It may slide upwards or suddenly jump to a higher level. In both cases, he is trying to get the stuck word unstuck, but again this is a sign that he needs help.

6. Struggle and Tension

Your child may struggle to get words out or have an unusual amount of tension in his lips, tongue, throat or chest when he tries to say certain words. At other times he may only have a small amount of necessary tension on the very same words. The degree of struggle may vary from being hardly noticeable to very obvious in certain speaking situations, and may disappear entirely for long periods of time. In any event, struggle and tension increase the chance that he will develop a persistent problem.

7. Moment of Fear

You may see a fleeting moment of fear in your child's face as he approaches a word that gives him trouble. If so, he has probably experienced enough difficulty getting stuck to make him react emotionally to the struggle or anticipation of trouble. He may go beyond momentary fear and begin to cry because he can't say a word. He may be afraid of particular words in certain speaking situations, or fear talking at all. If you can help your child when the fear is still a brief passing experience, there is a good chance of preventing more devastating emotional reactions to stuttering from developing.

8. Avoidance

The struggle to speak and fear the child experiences in talking may soon lead him to try a variety of avoidances. He may postpone trying a word until he is sure he can say it fluently. You may notice an unusual number and length of pauses. He may refuse to talk at times, substituting or inserting irrelevent words or meaningless noises until he is ready to say a word. He will continue to have normal delays in speaking as he tries to choose words or formulate sentences but these may now become exaggerated. If he does not speak even when it is clear that he knows what he wants to say, he is probably avoiding because of his growing fears.

These last five warning signs have been discussed separately but they often occur together. Fear reactions and avoidance are frequently accompanied by struggle and tension; tremors are due to excess tension.

These eight indicators differ from normal interruptions of speech in two ways. The first three—multiple repetitions, the schwa vowel, and prolongations—distort speech patterns. Many children make these distortions but this does not detract seriously from communication. In some children, however, they are very noticeable, and when used frequently and in many speaking situations, they should be recognized as signs of beginning stuttering. The next five—the stuttering tremor, rise in pitch and loudness, struggle and tension, the moment of fear, and avoidance —occur when your child begins to react to interruptions in his speech. These behaviors seriously inhibit the flow of speech and disturb communication. They indicate that your child is trying to do something about the interruptions. He may not be aware that he is doing these things for they are automatic responses. Although some of the avoidances and tension may seem helpful to him at first, they are harmful in the long run because they add distracting elements to his speech and tend to increase his fear of words. These disturbing extras eventually distress both your child and his listeners.

The presence of these signs indicate that your child may develop a real stuttering problem unless something is done. If you have not already done so, you should have your child examined by a clinician. He will work out an appropriate program of treatment with your child or may prefer to observe him a bit longer instead.

If you would like to observe your child's speech more closely over a period of time, there are certain things you should be aware of. As in other areas of development, speech does not progress evenly; you should expect to notice more difficulty at some times than at others. Note particularly the periods of more fluent speech to avoid becoming anxious about the occasional difficulty. Don't try to observe him every time he opens his mouth. Listen to what he is trying to tell you. Try to judge the amount of difficulty he is having and whether the speech is getting better or worse on the whole. When the clinician suggests that you listen for particular things, try to do so in a detached manner rather than as the child's parent. This may be difficult but it can be learned.

Why Does a Young Child Stutter?

This is a frustrating question because in spite of the many things we know about stuttering, we cannot provide a clear-cut answer. It is best to start our response with "We don't know, but..." It seems that children stutter for many reasons which vary from one child to the next. Stuttering sometimes continues when early causes are no longer in effect. Evidence shows that some children have basic problems managing the fine coordination and timing sequences of the movements needed for fluent speech, especially during the early years. Lack of coordination in speech may cause disfluency just as poor coordination of large muscles may cause stumbling while learning to walk. Stuttering may continue as the child learns to control speech muscles, although in some children it may fade away. This leads us to believe that some other unknown factor must account for the continued development of stuttering.

Similarly, certain kinds of emotional stress—either a single very disturbing event or a continuing pattern of stress—can disrupt speech patterns in most of us. The young child is particularly vulnerable because he is still learning to manage his emotions and many things seem threatening to him. Speech disruptions may become a symptom of inner conflict and anxiety. The child may begin to fear certain speaking situations because in his mind they are similar to others in which he has had difficulty. Not all children who undergo similar experiences begin to stutter however.

Normal disfluencies that every child has may of themselves be a source of difficulty. The child himself or those around him may react to these disfluencies in such a way that he feels compelled to eliminate them. The more he tries to do so, the worse they become, and the more unfavorably others react to them. A vicious circle begins and he is soon caught up in a way of talking that he feels he can no longer control.

You may have wondered if your child could be stuttering because of an intensely frightening experience. Although this could be the reason for some initial disruption in speech, it usually has only a temporary effect and causes stuttering in very few people. Can stuttering be "caught" through imitiation? Most of the evidence leads us to conclude that it seldom if ever starts in this way.

Stuttering does tend to run in families, but does this mean it is inherited? This could indicate some kind of organic basis. Some scientists have found what seems to be a genetic basis for speech interruptions which may, in turn, develop into stuttering, but for many stutterers this factor may not be important.

You see that we cannot say, "This is why young children stutter," but we do know many of the things that make it develop into a serious problem. Some of these things concern the child himself; but others involve your attitudes and behavior.

How Does the Child Who Stutters Compare With Those Who Do Not?

Aside from his stuttering, he is perfectly normal. Stutterers range in intelligence just as the rest of us do—some are dull, some are bright, and most are somewhere in between. Researchers have diligently sought for physical and psychological differences between stutterers and non-stutterers. The few differences that have been found are very subtle and are contradicted by similar studies. They do not appear consistently in all those who stutter. In older stutterers, any psychological differences between stutterers and non-stutterers are related to the stuttering and may very well be the result rather than the cause of the problem. The young child, at least, seems to be as well adjusted as his non-stuttering friends. He may have some emotional problems but they may or may not be related to the way he speaks.

What are Some Additional Facts about Stuttering?

Stutterers account for about one percent of the population, but a higher percentage of young children go through a temporary period of stuttering. Although this percentage is small, it does mean several million people in this country stutter at some point in their development.

We know that approximately four boys stutter for every girl. Many theories have been proposed to account for this ratio, and although some are quite plausible, we still do not know the answer.

Stress and anxiety almost always aggravate stuttering in a young child. For this reason many suggestions for helping your child are aimed at reducing these as much as possible. The difficulty lies in finding out your child's source of anxiety and stress. We do recognize that when pressure is released, there is often an almost magical return to normal fluency in many young children. Perhaps this kind of recovery is related to the fact that many children stop stuttering without any treatment or special attention at all or even while continuing to live under deplorable conditions. It has been estimated that for every person who stutters today, there are three other people who have stuttered at some point in their development. The reasons these people or their parents give for their recovery are extremely varied and not usually very helpful to us. Does this mean that they outgrew the stuttering? Any answer to this depends on what you consider to be the cause of stuttering. If you think stuttering is caused by an underdeveloped nervous and muscular system, children can outgrow it. But emotional reactions to speech difficulty are learned and not outgrown. The child who has learned these reactions and behaviors must somehow learn to change his behavior. Many authorities consider stuttering to be learned reactions and behaviors which can be unlearned.

We know that the frequency and severity of stuttering usually varies with time and circumstance. Sometimes the child will talk without difficulty, usually when he is speaking to himself, to pets or while singing. The stuttering may disappear completely for relatively long periods of time and then return in full force. This usually happens when stress and anxiety increase, but it is not always possible to pinpoint the source of anxiety.

We also know that many of the old traditional methods of reacting to stuttering do not help. In fact, they usually aggravate the problem. Telling him to "Talk slowly", to "Take a deep breath", to "Relax" are examples of useless and even harmful suggestions. Instructions to "Say it again" may result in his saying it fluently but this does not help the basic problem. Even more harmful are loud orders such as "Stop that!" combined with harsh looks and punishment. These methods are based on false assumptions about the nature of stuttering: that it is simply a bad habit which he can stop if he really tries, and never need to do again, or that he is deliberately being perverse and irritating, or that he "doesn't know how to talk right".

How You Can Help

Our suggestions for you vary greatly. Some are explicit instructions; others provide directions to take but leave the details to you; still others are a general discussion of ways in which the way you look at the problem can deepen your understanding or modify the way you feel. Your understanding and judgment in using any suggestion inevitably affect relations with your child. Remember that the way you do something is as important as what you do, and that no simple instructions to "do" or "don't" will be effective unless they are based on what you believe. The intereaction between you and your child is unique.

Helping Your Child to Speak More Smoothly

Our suggestions are directly related to your child's ability to speak fluently and to interact freely with others. If you are concerned about your child's speech, the following suggestions are particularly important, but they also encourage the social development of any child.

All the topics discussed involve direct changes in your own behavior and attitudes. This does not imply that if your child begins to stutter, it is your fault. Stuttering is not due to one circumstance or one person; it may be affected by many subtle and fleeting causes. The difficulty may be present one moment and gone the next. Most of the time your child may speak very much like other children, but sometimes he may seem more anxious and aware of his stumbling speech.

The one thing you can control and modify is that most important part of his environment: **you.** For many very young children, certain changes in you and other members of the family are the most effective way to encourage normal fluency.

Speech Interactions

In order to help you begin to talk with your child in constructive ways, let us review briefly what to expect between the ages of two and six. This period represents an explosion of growth and development. By the age of two, your child can be expected to use words and short sentences with some consistency. By the age of six, he will be using long sentences and will have increased his vocabulary immensely. He will also have begun to learn the power of voice and words to control the behavior of others and to express his feelings. He will be using speech extensively in his social interactions. His basic value system—what is good and bad—will crystallize in many ways. He will have acquired greater opportunities to come and go, to climb and explore, to laugh and cry, and even to accept some responsibility for his own care and welfare. Many new doors are opening rapidly and speech plays a central role in all of these. Not only must your child be able to be understood, he must also be able to say what he wants, when he wants. It is in this light that the following suggestions should be considered.

Listen With "All Ears"

It may surprise you that the process of listening should be given special attention. Of course you listen to your child; it's hard not to as he reaches the stage of chattering or questioning you constantly. You are probably already aware that you listen selectively, for your own protection if for no other reason. We can help you to do this selective listening in ways that do not give your child the impression that you never listen or don't want to listen to him. Furthermore, you can learn to become more perceptive to what is important to your child and his development.

Some systematic attention to the listening process itself as well as to your personal listening habits will give you richer, deeper communication with your child. Try to carry through the following four-step procedure over several days.

1. For the first two or three days, concentrate from time to time on evaluating just how you listen to him, how much and how often. What kind of topics get your attention? Note the variations in the intensity of your listening: from hearing only a small part of what he is saying to full attention to almost every word. Do you let him finish before you start talking? Do you hurry him when he tries to talk? What proportion of his chatter do you actually hear? How much does he talk and what does he talk to you about? How do you react when he interrupts you when you are doing or saying something that is important? How often do you look at him when you are actively listening? Jot down some notes if you think it would help you. This attention to the way in which you listen will provide the basis for the next three steps.

2. For the next day or two, try to change the balance of your listening. You cannot listen attentively every time he opens his mouth, nor should you, particularly if he talks a great deal, but you may decide that more or less attention is better. You may change the intensity of listening in situations in which you did not listen attentively before. If necessary, alter the way you react when he interrupts you. The important thing is to learn that you can modify your listening habits without going to extremes.

3. For the next few days, make a conscious but not continuous effort to listen for more than just the literal meaning of words when he is talking to you or to others. What is he saying

besides the words? Your child is always sending you emotional and implied messages. Notice how he uses his voice to do this, with inflections on words, pauses, repetitions, the timing of words and the way he looks or doesn't look at you.

Does he talk in a whining tone with you but not with others? Does he sound fearful with some members of the family? Do you frequently detect that querulous upward inflection in "Mommy" as he seeks attention? Does he repeat words more often with some people than with others? When he talks to dolls or imaginary playmates, does he use confident authoritative tones that are in contrast to the way he speaks to people?

Preoccupation with certain topics or questions may indicate underlying fears.

Does he ask a series of questions over a period of several days about the same general topic, such as sickness, accidents, or about what he should do "If... ?" Does he ask the same question repeatedly when you are sure that he knows the answer? This may indicate a need for your attention.

These three steps should help you to listen in a more understanding way and to react more appropriately to both literal word meanings and the important feelings behind them. This is the essence of good communication. As you become more aware of the need to both listen and not listen, you will find ways to let him know that your attention to daily duties does not mean you don't love him. Deliberately interrupt your other activities at times in order to express your love and interest.

4. As a final step, try to identify any signal that your child sends out indicating an immediate need for intensive listening. These usually occur long before the noisy crying stage. These

may take a long time to recognize because these occasions do not occur often. When they do occur, be alert to facial expressions, postures, and movements expressing withdrawal. The need for listening may be indicated vocally by a drastic change in loudness or unusual hesitations and repetitions.

Because listening is such an important part of the communication process and because it is directly related to emotion, improving your listening habits should have a direct effect on your child's fluency. Remember that listening should be a rewarding and joyful experience—not a burden.

Talk *With* Rather Than *At* Your Child

The way in which you talk is closely related to the listening process. At times, your child seems to need a continual talking **at**: you must inform him, set rules, reproach him and otherwise control his behavior with your voice and words. In spite of yourself, you will find that you are talking **at** him most of the time. It is not surprising that some children are more sensitive than others to this barrage. You can help prevent an adverse reaction by making conscious efforts to counteract the amount of talking **at** by an increase in the periods of talking **with**, during which there is a true interchange of ideas and feelings. Balanced in this way, talking becomes a sharing experience that is pleasant for both of you.

First listen to yourself for a day to determine how much of your contact with your child is talking **at**. Then deliberately set up more time and topics for talking with him. Ask him questions about things that do not involve his behavior. If he can do so easily, let him tell you what he has experienced during the day; but if this is difficult for him, never force it. Let him know that you can listen patiently. Contribute to the conversation, making sure that your comments do not include judgment or criticism. This sets the stage for the best fluency of which he is capable.

Provide an Appropriate Speech Model for Your Child

We assume that you are trying to provide examples of good speech for your child, and that you speak clearly and use appropriate words for objects and events. We hope you use sentences and vocabulary appropriate for his age. Do you habitually talk too rapidly and fluently? If so, he may be attempting to imitate you although he does not yet have the verbal facility to do so, and thus naturally stumbles and hesitates. If you think this is the case, make an effort to talk more slowly. Pause more often. If your sentences tend to be long, complex, or rambling, your child will probably have trouble understanding you and may feel uncertain as to how to respond. This can in turn lead to disfluencies when he replies. Try simpler and shorter sentences, at least part of the time. Do you tend to interrupt him or cut off the ends of his sentences because you know what he is going to say? This also adds unnecessary pressure. Give him time; you can learn to act and speak with more patience.

Provide Pleasurable Rewarding Speech Experiences

You have already begun to make speaking a pleasure for your child when you listen in the way we have described, but you can do more. Even in the first year of life, you should associate your own talking with pleasant activities. Singing while holding or rocking him is pleasant for both of you. Talk with him more about what you are doing. The more verbal fun you can have in the family, the more quickly your child will learn that speaking can be a pleasure. This should help to offset the many times that speech must be used to scold, reprimand, or punish. At certain times, be sure that the family pays attention to what he is saying even if it means controlling some of the brothers and sisters. After all, they need to learn to let others talk instead of always seizing attention. If he in turn begins to monopolize the conversation, he too may need to learn to let others speak. The important point is to avoid too many frustrating experiences.

Read or Tell Stories to Him

Reading aloud and story-telling also emphasize the pleasurable side of speech communication. They are important enough for some special attention. Read aloud to your child with reasonable frequency and regularity. When you have read the same favorite stories many times, let him finish some of the sentences or tell the story to you in his own words, but only if he wants to. If you feel you do not have a knack for making up stories, begin with favorite pictures, preferably those with a story behind them. Tell him about events from your own life when you were little or when he was smaller. All children love this. Avoid frightening stories; they are disturbing even though he may enjoy them. You should be able to find an opportunity every day for "reading" pictures or telling stories at a time when there are few or no interruptions. If you find yourself in competition with the television, have a fixed hour to turn it off.

Help Him to Express His Feelings Verbally

How often do you tell your child that you love or like him? It will be difficult for him to learn to express these very important feelings if you do not set the example.

What do you laugh at? If you tend to laugh at things which hurt others, you are teaching him to do the same. Since he knows that cruelty is not a laughing matter, he will be confused. If you use this kind of humor and at the same time demand that he avoid hurting others both physically and psychologically, the resulting conflict will become another possible source of uncertainty and disfluency. He needs to learn that there are several kinds of laughter, so talk with him about what made you laugh. Laugh at funny things, not at hurtful things.

The next time he expresses rage or anger, take the necessary time to listen to him. Discuss what it was that made him angry. There may be many reasons: frustration, a head-strong demand to have his own way, a genuine feeling of hurt, or perhaps an imitation of your own displays of anger or fatigue. With understanding, talk with him about better ways to express his feelings. Show him that he can obtain what he really wants without displays of temper, and give him concrete examples of how he might have expressed himself more constructively. When he has found better ways of expressing his feelings, the internal conflicts causing some of his disfluencies will be reduced.

Nonverbal Communication

Words are not the only way to convey meaning. A fundamental sense of well-being, or lack of it, depends upon an array of non-verbal communication between you and your child.

Most people think of communication as solely verbal—words expressing thoughts or ideas. But it is far more. Perhaps you already know this but tend to forget its importance as your child grows older. Even before your child began to talk, he jabbered in a pattern that sounded like speech, but with no understandable words. Nevertheless, he was communicating with you. If you responded to this, you both undoubtedly felt deep satisfaction. As your child grows older, he continues to use first nonsense, then recognizable words for this same emotional communication. Adults do the same; real words actually become non-words. We repeat statements over and over, even when we know our listeners have heard us say them before. We say "G'Morning" without any thought to the meaning of each word. This is our way of reaching out to others. If you listen carefully, you realize that your child often uses speech to reach out and make contact: "Mommy, I've got something in my eye!" "Daddy, see this big scratch on my leg?" Your specific answers to these questions are not as important as noticing and paying attention. Does he ask the same questions over and over? Does he intrude while you are particularly busy with a question to which you are sure he knows the answer? As you become more sensitive to the emotional communication which underlies so much of this kind of speech, you can respond in a more meaningful and appropriate way.

Seek Ways to Express Positive Feelings Nonverbally

Look at him and smile whenever you can. If he asks why you are smiling, tell him it is because you love him. Occasionally touch or pat him as he goes by you; the look on your face as well as your words will express your pride in him. Help him to do difficult things cheerfully but never demand verbal gratitude from him.

Analyzing Vocal Patterns

Listen to his and to your own inflections, loudness, and pitch levels when you talk with him to see what they tell you about the emotions underlying speech. You may need to analyze your own emotions to be able to do this. Listen to others talking when you are not involved in the conversation. Turn on a tape recorder and let it run until you have forgotten it is there; then listen to selected portions. What are you listening for? Perhaps you already know how much louder you speak when you are angry with your child or with the world in general. You may find that you speak in a higher pitched voice which at times becomes very harsh and grating. You may even notice unusual pitch patterns—upward and downward inflections—as you try to be patient but struggle to control your irritation. Downward inflections and less volume may indicate that you have given up trying to help your child. At times, you may hear a condescending tone or a talking down to him. Perhaps your voice patterns are not extreme, but they are always the same when you speak to your child and usually different when you talk to others. Do you use a similar tone in speaking to your dog and to your child? Try to make modifications in your own speech in a way that emphasizes positive, constructive feelings.

19

Provide Time for Closeness

You have no doubt treasured those moments when you have felt especially close to your child. These often occur when words between you are few; when you are doing something together—taking a walk, baking a cake, fixing something—that demands little or no speech. If these moments occur often, even if they are brief, they will help him to feel more secure, and stuttering will usually decrease. These quiet happy times will occur accidentally, but you can create more of them. It may involve no more than sharing his play with blocks, picking up toys with him for a few moments, or walking together through the park. Not all the things you plan will produce the level of closeness you want, since this is spontaneous; but you can gradually build a relationship that makes him aware of being wanted and loved without a constant flow of words. Words of love without the nonverbal demonstration of it are hollow and a child soon learns this.

Day-to-Day Living

There is more to bringing up your child than talking with him. A young life is filled with a variety of opportunities to grow more strong and secure or to feel more threatened and weak. We will not try to provide you with a comprehensive manual on all the problems of parenthood, but certain aspects of it contain many possibilities for promoting fluency.

Meal Time

If your child is a fussy eater, and mealtime is a problem for both of you, you may want to re-examine the situation. Does he stutter more at mealtime? What conflicts occur? Are you talking at him or scolding frequently? We suggest that you first examine your own demands. Are you worried that he is not getting enough of the right things? If he is provided with good food and is not nagged to eat it without snacks just before meals, he will eventually get hungry enough to eat what he needs. If he tends to lose his appetite at the usual time and place for meals, try changing things around for awhile. Are you too concerned about how he eats? If you feel you must teach him manners, do it as a game while he is eating a dish of ice cream. The rest of the time, control your impulse to correct him. Are you confusing eating and drinking with discipline? He will always win this struggle—at great cost to himself and to you—because you cannot make him eat. Don't try; all you will do is to make everyone miserable. You can control where and when he eats, and that is enough. If you are now using mealtime to discuss your adult problems, this can be done at a different time.

Going to Bed

You can't make him go to sleep either, and if you try, you may find that he is in control of the going-to-bed process. The key to achieving reasonable regularity lies in being consistent and avoiding many of the irrelevant activities that become associated with the process. We are sure that you know many of the delaying tactics he uses to add to an already complicated ritual. Don't add any more; the simpler the better. Evening is often a good time to read to him, but this can be done earlier than at the last minute. Hold him in your arms as a way of calming him just before he goes to bed.

Toilet Problems

Since you can't make him go to the toilet or control all the accidents, don't try. If you have been too anxious to toilet train him too early, this probably has not succeeded. If bed-wetting continues to be a problem, it is important to treat it in such a way that he is not made to feel that he is a failure. You can help him see that the mess it creates is irritating but that you accept him: not in spite of it, but because he is a part of you. By reducing his feelings of guilt, you make it easier for him and for yourself in the long run.

21

General Behavior

Self-doubts and feelings of failure arise when you make demands on your child to measure up to some ideal image. Are you demanding a level of perfection that is too high? You will recall that more boys stutter than girls. Some psychologists feel that part of this difference comes from our cultural expectations for boys. A boy is expected to act like a man too soon. If he cries for reasons not approved of for boys, you may think that he is not measuring up. Don't make him feel guilty. Speech difficulties often arise during such episodes and may become conditioned to these feelings.

We sometimes expect certain social phrases even if the words are parroted without much meaning. If you expect your child to always be at his best, you are expecting too much. Have tolerance for his age and interests, for his human frailty. Certainly we hope you do not use those devastating and demeaning remarks made by some parents to cover their embarassment when the child does not say "How do you do?" or some other social phrase. After all, he is still a little child. If you are embarassed by such behavior on his part, your expectations are too high.

How do you handle his outbursts of anger? Obviously some controls are necessary. He needs to learn to manage this emotion effectively. If you treat it as something to be suppressed, the speech disfluencies that often occur at this time will become exaggerated in his mind. Any method you use to control him should avoid making him feel that he is bad because he has the emotion. Don't shame him in any way. You can calmly discuss his behavior afterward and explain that there are many other ways to cope with his feelings. This will help to emphasize the difference between **having** a feeling and what one **does** with it.

Your child's expressions of aggression and hostility can be handled in such a way that other problems do not develop. It is imperative that he eventually learn to manage these feelings in relatively constructive ways. If you make him feel guilty and ashamed, you are teaching him that he is bad. What can a child do with such knowledge but be miserable and uncertain? Perhaps you believe that one should feel guilty and ashamed about having such feelings. If so, you are unconsciously passing on to him the way that you were probably brought up. If you feel guilty because you have these feelings, or if you have not discovered how to control and release them yourself, you will have difficulty teaching your child how to do so. Here you may need to change your own behavior. Listen to your own language when you are angry with your child. Regardless of how you handle the immediate crisis, how do you follow up? He needs explanations in order to know what you wanted to teach him when you were angry. You should help him to understand that you needed to release your own feelings. One way or another, he needs an explanation. Don't expect him to change his reactions at once— he needs time and experience—but encourage any improvement.

Brothers and Sisters

If your child has brothers or sisters, you are well aware of how much they can help or hinder his development. They stimulate him to talk—and then they won't give him a chance to do it. Your children all compete for your attention in their own individual ways, and the one who speaks the quickest and loudest often succeeds in getting it. The child with a tendency to stutter often needs to have some controls put on the rest of the family to make sure he has a fair opportunity to speak. If he is inclined to be more withdrawn and hesitant than the others, he needs support from you more often. This does not mean that he should always be allowed to talk, nor should you have rigid rules that the other children never interrupt him. Be sensible. If you are overprotective, he will begin to do more of whatever it is that gives him the advantage over others. You need to be flexible in determining when you need to protect his right to talk. When he has a crisis of any kind, he should get more attention, just as each of the other children should, but the crisis must be real and not manufactured. When in doubt, give him the attention.

Although they communicate in different ways, all of your children should have a chance to be heard. These differences are desirable; they give your children distinct personalities. This attitude towards differences should carry over to those outside the family as well. Avoid using differences in personal characteristics to demean or downgrade anyone. If you despise people who are afraid or deride someone who is crippled, in effect you are telling your child that differences are bad. His own differences, such as difficulty in speaking, will then assume vast proportions.

Discipline

There are some general guidelines to follow which will affect your child's feelings toward himself and others. Anything that gives him a feeling of being a failure will make him hesitate in speaking. At the same time, you need to teach him to behave appropriately and to act in ways that are reasonably comfortable for you and the rest of the family. The way in which you do this will have a direct influence on his feelings about himself.

The way you use speech to punish or reward him is also important. Words and expressions can be used to whip your child. In so doing you may reduce him to a level that is easy to control, but the cost is too high. If you have violent punishing outbursts, how does he react? Does he freeze or look as if he is terribly afraid? Or do you completely miss his reaction because you are so angry? In either case, you are using your emotion as a club to force him to behave. This approach may work for a time but only at the sacrifice of his security. Another emotional club

24

some parents use is: "If you love me and want me to love you, you must always do what I want you to do." It's better to let him know that if he continues to act in unlovable ways, you won't have much of a chance to express your love.

Examine all your methods of discipline: rewards and punishments. To what degree do they represent an objective and loving attitude on your part? Try to avoid methods that are too emotional, too prolonged, or too cold and stern. Use your own good judgment to decide when you really need to be consistent. You don't want to be too erratic or random about your disciplining, nor do you want to be too rigid.

Pressure

Examine the daily activities in which your child is involved. Is there so much going on that he is bounced from one thing to another simply because the rest of the family is so involved in them? If he goes to nursery school, what is his schedule there? How can you complement it at home so that he gets necessary rest and activity? Does he have periodic quiet times at school and at home, or does he have so much time to himself that he gets over-excited when there is someone to pay attention to him? Is he with adults most of the time? What kind of balance does he have between rest and activity? These questions can lead you to ways of making his environment one that is stimulating without being too demanding. Remember that any attitude or behavior of yours that tends to make him feel guilty, ashamed, frustrated, inadequate, rejected or anxious place him under pressure that often shows up in difficulty with the smooth flow of words. Such presures can be further reduced.

Other Influences

We have said that painful, traumatic incidents do not usually cause stuttering, but family tragedies naturally upset any child. In spite of your efforts to protect him, events such as illness, emotional conflict and accidents are sure to happen. They may be accompanied by a greater number of hesitations and repetitions in your child's speech. If so, accept this as normal; don't add to his concern by reacting to his stuttering. If family conflicts continue, he may have more disfluencies. To counteract this, intensify your loving relationship with him. If the family moves to a new house or town, you may find increased disfluencies arising from your preoccupation with the move and adjustment to new surroundings. If you take extra time and effort at these difficult times, your child's speech will probably return to its usual level of fluency.

If you or anyone else in the family stutters, you may be quite worried when he shows signs of having trouble. As we have said earlier, he is not likely to imitate the one who stutters, although if he strongly identifies with him, he may try to be like him in many ways. If your child is not showing the severe warning signs however, try to accept any disfluencies as normal rather than as the beginnings of inherited stuttering.

Special holidays, up-coming vacations, or starting pre-school are exciting times, but they can be too stimulating for a young child. Parents often tell us that their child was fluent all summer but began to have trouble just before school started. If you notice less fluency during these times, you should try to reduce the intensity of the situation. Sometimes the source of trouble is a high peak of excitement that lasts over too long a period of time. Christmas Day can cause a combination of high excitement plus vague disappointment or frustration. One family handled this problem by taking most of the day to open presents. As each child opened a present, he would have time to play with the toy, try on his new clothes, or have part of a new book read to him. In this way, excitement was kept at a more pleasurable level. The children were not frustrated by too much too fast.

Your efforts to persuade your child to make specific statements can disrupt his fluency. You may want him to tell you what has happened in a situation or merely to tell Aunt Martha something interesting. In doing so, you are putting a great deal of pressure on him without realizing it. This can be avoided by letting him proceed at his own rate. Is it really so important that he tell Aunt Martha at all?

It is easy to interrupt someone who has many hesitancies in his speech, but if your child is showing signs of stuttering, this is to be avoided. If he is interrupted too often, he needs extra consideration from you and the family. You should not attempt to completely eliminate interruptions, but it is necessary to reduce them. Be alert for times when what he is saying is of special importance to him, and try to avoid any interruptions then.

Look for other things that make it difficult for him to be as fluent as he can. Does he have more trouble when talking and doing something else at the same time? Encourage him to stop the other activity when he wants to speak. If he is hurt while playing, don't ask for explanations until he has calmed down. With some effort, you will be able to find many situations throughout the day when a little change in the way you do things will make it easier for him to speak more fluently.

Take a look at his development on the whole: physical skills and coordination, social skills, emotional and intellectual development. You may find that he is showing a special interest or rapid growth in any of these areas. If so, it may mean that his energy and attention will not be on speech skills for a time. His speech development is temporarily put aside so that he can concentrate on other areas. Speech may appear to be less fluent than it was a few months before or all his development may hit a general plateau. If this happens, try not to worry. Development is not a continuous and steady process; growth often occurs in spurts. If this kind of plateau lasts too long, naturally you should look for reasons. You may then want to consult professional help. But if you see that he is intensely interested in learning to ride a tricycle, don't worry if his speech is set aside for awhile.

We have provided some general guidelines and a few specific suggestions for constructive ways of relating to your child. We hope you will be reasonably thoughtful and consistent in what you do, but we do not want to impose rigid patterns. One mother was advised to establish a routine to give her son a sense of security. She set up such a tight schedule from 7 a.m. through 8 p.m. that every half hour had exactly the same activity every day. Needless to say, this routine created additional problems. A reasonable schedule and more relaxation on the part of the mother resulted in much improved fluency. Avoid extremes. Pay attention to the effects of whatever you do and be ready to make adjustments in your actions and expectations when you see the need.

Helping the Child Who Stutters

You may have a child who worries you because for some reason or another, he seems to be much less fluent than you think he should be. Whether he is stuttering or not, you can be substantially reassured by the suggestions we have already provided. However, it may already be apparent to you and to the clinician that your child is much more disfluent than he is expected to be at his age. He may repeat whole words or exhibit other signs of stuttering too frequently. In this case you will need to pay special attention to certain additional procedures. The suggestions that follow are ways of encouraging better fluency and preventing the development of severe stuttering. If you need more specifics for your unique situation, the clinician can help you.

Accept the Disfluencies

You probably have difficulty accepting your child's hesitant speech because you are afraid that he will develop life-long stuttering. Even if you try to react unemotionally, the underlying feelings and attitudes will show through and have an effect on your child. To combat this, you will need to develop an understanding of all kinds of disfluencies, many of which are very common in everyday speech.

Study Speech Differences

Listen to the speech of other children and adults now and then, particularly when they are not talking to you. Count the disfluencies: any stoppage in the flow of words such as repetitions, backtracking, pauses or insertions of extraneous noises.

Become aware of how much disfluency appears in normal speech. Notice, too, how many different types of disfluency there are. Pauses are often used for emphasis, grammatical clarity, or for thinking and are perfectly normal interruptions. If you listen to your own breaks in fluency, you will find yourself becoming very sensitive to them. You will be impressed by how often disfluencies occur as part of everyone's general flow of speech.

Your child probably has more of these breaks in fluency than you do. You should note the variation and frequency of these. There will be times when even the child you are worried about will be perfectly fluent. This should reassure you because it shows you that he really does know how to talk and that with continued practice he can improve, although he cannot be perfect all the time—nor should he be. As a result, you will begin to consider disfluencies in a different perspective.

Increase Your Tolerance for Disfluencies

The same amount of disfluency that causes one listener to become nervous may not even be noticed by another. If you find that your child's disfluencies continue to disturb you, you should try to increase your tolerance of them. Asking yourself the following questions should lead you to a greater acceptance. Why are you irritated or upset when your child takes longer to say something than you think he should? Aren't you expecting a level of fluency he cannot meet? Why do you expect him to speak more fluently than he does? Because other children his age are more fluent, or because your other children are? Why must he develop just as they do? Is it because you don't want to take the necessary time to hear what he has to say? **The best way to improve your relationship with him is to take the necessary time.** Are you still worried that he may get worse? Do you feel that his hesitant speech is a sign of basic inferiority? Are you worried about what will happen to him when he goes to school? All this may simply be adding to the trouble he is having.

Express Acceptance

Let us assume that you are ready to accept his disfluencies. What does this mean? Some people advise parents to ignore the disfluencies. We feel that there are more positive elements in the idea of acceptance however. How do you show that you accept someone else's behavior? Essentially you say to yourself, "I notice that he is doing this but it doesn't matter. My feelings toward him have not changed. Most of the time I don't even notice." Acceptance is a combination of marginal awareness and neutral feelings. You recognize that many skills develop at different rates in children but you don't react to these differences until they become extreme. Even then you usually don't do anything until a problem has lasted a long time.

One mother improved her acceptance of her child's broken speech by reviewing how she had reacted when he was learning to eat with a spoon. He fumbled and spilled food many times in a process that took several months and was still not perfect when she told us of this experience. She recalled that she had not been upset by his awkwardness; she considered it normal and was pleased when he succeeded. As the weeks passed, the spills became fewer but some meals were still mild disasters. Gradually the child became quite proficient and she could accept his occasional difficulties without emotion. She realized that she should react to his speech development in the same way.

We realize how difficult it may be for you to carry out these instructions if your child is stuttering severely. It may help you to remember that **he is doing the best he can**. When you react emotionally, you make him struggle harder to stop, avoid, or conceal his stuttering, and this makes it worse. Don't make his problem more complex than it already is.

31

Avoid the Label "Stuttering" for Disfluencies

There will be some exceptions but let us first look at some of the reasons for this advice We have pointed out that many kinds of disfluencies are normal even though they may occur quite frequently. It is only after they change in character and are accompanied by awareness, fear and struggle on the part of your child that they become real stuttering. Only then should you identify them by this label when talking with him. If these extra reactions are not occurring, it is not helpful to call his disfluencies stuttering because stuttering is a complex and disturbing speaking disorder. One prominent theory of stuttering is that it begins because those around the child react to his normal disfluencies as if they were abnormal; so he tries to prevent and avoid them. The harder he tries, the more disfluently he speaks and the vicious circle begins. We do not feel that the labeling of normal hesitations and repetitions as stuttering is the sole source of the disorder or that this labeling will inevitably result in stuttering. But there is no doubt that it is more difficult for you to accept his disfluencies without undue reaction if you continuously think of all of them as stuttering. It will no doubt add pressure when he attempts to speak. Avoiding this label should help you to react appropriately when he talks, and thus leave him greater freedom to develop his speech skills.

We also recognize that this distinction between normal disfluencies and stuttering or abnormal disfluencies is not always made by the public in general. People often say "I stutter once in awhile myself" or "Everyone stutters" when they are actually referring to normal disfluencies. Perhaps you or others in the family have already labeled your child's speech stuttering or called him a stutterer. In this case you should not make a desperate and sudden effort to never mention these words again. It would help if you tried to avoid using them for the reasons given above. Use descriptive terms instead of a label. Explain that he is repeating certain words, sounds or syllables or that he is hesitating, interrupting his speech, stopping, pausing or inserting extra sounds. Any of these expressions can take on a negative connotation if used with vocal inflections or facial expressions which designate them as undesirable. The word disfluency, which we have used throughout this book, is intended to be a neutral term but could well become as negative as the label stuttering if used in the wrong way.

If your child struggles intensely and often with his disfluencies and shows anxiety and fear, you will need to do more than simply accept his speech. You should continue to use as many descriptive terms as possible when discussing stuttering with him. If you notice tense muscles, eye blinks, reluctance to attempt words, mouth postures with no sound coming out or similar behaviors, you could tell him that he struggles or works too hard. At the same time you should not make special efforts to conceal the label from him if everyone else is thinking of his speech as stuttering. **Complete avoidance of the word in these circumstances makes him more anxious, not less. It isn't the words which are bad but the way in which they are used.**

One term should be avoided. Try not to see him as "a stutterer". There is a subtle but critical difference between "He is a stutterer" and "He stutters". The former sets him apart as a separate and inferior person. The latter says he is **doing** something just as he does a lot of things.

Reduce Your Anxiety

We are aware of your difficulty in listening to your child stutter and of your natural anxiety about him. One mother who brought her child to the speech clinic expressed how worn out and overwhelmed she felt as he struggled with his speech. Difficult as it may seem, you can do something about your own anxiety. Remember that approximately 75 per cent of all children who stutter do not continue to do so after childhood. Your understanding help and support when the problem is still in its early stages greatly increases the probability that he will achieve normal fluency. Your ability to look at his stuttering objectively and to understand what he is doing—and we can all modify or change the way we do things—should help you to reduce your anxiety. Your efforts to determine its severity and consistency give you something positive to work on. Be conscious of your increasing ability to observe his stuttering calmly and to refrain from becoming tense or alarmed when he suddenly stutters. Concentrate on what is happening **now** and not on what might happen in years to come. Determine how much fluency he has. If you count his words for a period of time, noting the difficulties, you will find that an overwhelming percentage of these words are perfectly normal—not all of them perfectly fluent, but certainly acceptable for his age. You have ample evidence here that he does know how to talk.

When the disturbing elements which increase his intermittant stuttering are reduced, he will be freer to talk without undue interruptions. In the meantime you and he have a problem that is best worked out if you are not too anxious.

React Appropriately to His Stuttering

How do you react "appropriately"? Most of the time, don't react at all. That is to say, be as neutral as you are to the fluent portion of his speech. Stuttering could become so disturbing to your child and so distracting that a total lack of reaction on your part would be inappropriate. In this case you should show him that you recognize what he did without showing any hint of surprise, criticism or pity. Nor should you suggest that he do something about it. You might say, "You really got stuck on that one", or "You worked hard on that word", or "It's no fun, is it?" These should be presented as statements of fact. Other times try a smile with a look and word that says "Sometimes words just don't come out easily". Occasionally his combinations of sounds and timing will be funny; laugh with him and go on with the conversation. You can even display mild sympathy for him. The vocal inflection and timing of these reactions are vital. In the speech clinic we often observe parents who have learned to handle this problem beautifully. One mother changed her horror of stuttering into an attitude of admiration for her son who managed to communicate well in spite of a severe problem, and this admiration was reflected in her voice. We appreciate how difficult this is when you are worried or feeling sorry for your child as he struggles, but don't add to his anxiety. You may need to work on your own feelings before you are able to react as we have outlined. We do not mean that you should stifle all feelings of sympathy for your child; just let this feeling come out in an attitude of constructive love that sees him as much more than "a stutterer". The problem is such a small part of what he is. It is just that—a problem which needs to be worked out like bed-wetting or nose-picking—all of which need to be managed sensibly.

Talk With Him About His Stuttering

Some clinicians work with the parents of stutterers without ever mentioning the problem to the child. There are times however, when you should go beyond the recognition-acceptance reaction to his stuttering. When he goes to a clinician, your child may need to be told that because he is having trouble with words "getting stuck", you would like to have an expert listen to him and try to find ways to help. He may ask questions about his speech, such as "Why can't I talk?" "Why do I get stuck?" or even "What's the matter with me?" At other times the look on your child's face when he is especially distressed might call for a positive response on your part. You may notice that he has the idea that stuttering should be hidden. Your bringing it out into the open should help him.

Answers to "Why do I stutter?" are the most difficult, but you can best satisfy him with short explanations. Here is an example of what you might tell him.

All of us get tangled up or stuck at times. Some of us do it more than others. Little children are more likely to hesitate because they are still learning to talk. They also stumble more when walking and running. When they have trouble speaking, they sometimes try too hard to stop and this makes it worse.

By calling his attention to stumblings in your own speech when they occur, you can help him to understand that all of us have trouble at times. Any question about whether or not something is the matter with him should be answered by "No" and followed by a fuller description of what is happening when he stutters. You can use these opportunities to reassure him that it is all right for him to get stuck if he feels he cannot speak any other way. The main idea is to be as descriptive as possible, to keep explanations simple and to avoid sounding mysterious or emotional.

Give Him Direct Advice at Times

After asking "Why?" your child may ask "How can I stop it?" The best suggestion is "Don't work so hard" or "Try to relax and loosen up the tightness". Tell him to try to talk as easily as he can at the moment. One parent demonstrated this idea by squeezing his fist and gradually relaxing it while letting a sound "leak out". You can show your child two ways of saying a word—the "hard" and the "easy" way to let the sound out.

If he needs to repeat words or sounds he should try to do so in a relaxed way; it is the struggle that makes things worse. If he says he cannot talk in any other way, give him the time he needs. Above all, do not become irritated when he does not or can not follow your advice.

Do not tell your child how not to stutter. Advice such as "Take a deep breath" or "Think of what you want to say before you speak" or "Slow down" will compound his problem in at least three ways: it implies that if he did something right, he would not stutter; it makes him feel guilty because he cannot make the advice work; and finally it often adds additional behaviors to his talking which distract him and his listeners and further impede the flow of speech.

Reduce His Fears, Anxieties and Frustrations with Speech

One of the best ways to do this is to encourage your child to talk about his fears, anxieties, and frustrations. This means that you must be prepared to accept how he feels without criticism or disapproval, regardless of how irrational they may seem to you. They are not signs of weakness or inadequacy; they show that he is human. One parent expressed his own fears, past and present, and was able to get the idea across to his son that fears are normal for everyone, and that we can all learn to reduce them. Many of your child's fears may not be directly related to talking, but they can still have an overall effect on him by making him more hesitant and withdrawn. Bringing his fears out in the open and reassuring your child that you accept him and his fears can greatly reduce their importance.

Avoid increasing your child's fears by overprotection. Don't do everything for him or arrange his life in such a way that he doesn't need to talk. If he will talk on the telephone, encourage it. Overprotection will eventually add to his fears of talking and stuttering.

There are additional ways to deal with your child's fears. Many parents allow their child to have a dim night light in his room to offset his fear of the dark. Try approaching that which causes him fear in steps, and stop temporarily when he shows any fear. Then move towards the source of fear when he is ready. Never force him; take the necessary time. One child would run from the room whenever visitors came to the home. His mother helped him by waiting until the guests were seated and talking, then she called the child to the door to get something from her; the first time it was a piece of cake she was serving. She then allowed him to leave the room without speaking. In later visits, the child was able to sit quietly in her lap for part of the visit and to say "Goodbye" when he left. The barriers were thus gradually overcome.

If your child encounters periods of very severe blocking and stuttering, he will probably build up a great deal of frustration. Many parents describe various ways of coping effectively with this. One father encouraged his son to hit Bobo the Clown as hard as he could until he felt better. Another talked with his son in private and allowed the child to say what he wanted without any disapproval, only reassurance that he understood the child's feelings. Still another had his son talk into a wastebasket to "throw out the poison". Outdoor exercise is also helpful in reducing tension.

We have outlined many things for you to do in order to ensure your child the best chance of developing normal fluency. As you carry out our suggestions, try to go a little further. Look for ways to give yourself to your child, not with a grim dedication to give yourself up just because he stutters, but for the mutual pleasure of being together. Do not seek or expect his appreciation. You are not doing him a favor for which you expect thanks but rather are fulfilling that which is his right as your child.

If we have not given you enough alternatives for action, ask the clinician for methods appropriate to your specific situation. If you create your own, they will probably work better than ours. Just try to keep in mind the general principles we have described for a constructive and positive relationship with your child.

As you read our suggestions, you may have wondered if we expect a greater change in you than in your child. You are right; the skill with which you use our suggestions will determine how successful your efforts are. The delicate interaction between parent and child is not subject to simple rules; neither is the relationship with the clinician who is helping your child. We realize that you have a more difficult role because as a parent you live with the result of your decisions and assume the ultimate responsibility. The ideas we have offered touch the roots of stuttering—and many other human problems. We are confident that a conscious effort on your part to follow these principles will benefit both you and your child.

If you want more information on this subject, you may wish to obtain:

Ainsworth, Stanley.
Stuttering: What It Is and What To Do About It.
Published by Cliff's Notes, Lincoln, Nebraska 68501. Paperback.

Ainsworth, Stanley. Positive Emotional Power.
Published by Prentice-Hall, Inc.,
Englewood Cliffs, New Jersey 07632. Paperback.

The Speech Foundation of America is a non-profit charitable organization dedicated to the prevention and relief of stuttering. If you feel that this book has helped you and you wish to help this cause, send a contribution to us at Box 11749, Memphis, Tennessee 38111. Contributions are tax deductible.